Never Tell A Lie

A shepherd named Kalu used to go to forest everyday to graze his goats.

The naughty shepherd did not like the lonliness of the forest. So, he used to play pranks daily.

One day, the naughty shepherd raised a false alarm, "Wolf ! Wolf ! Save me!! Hel..l..l..p !!!"

The farmers working in the
nearby fields ran to help the
shepherd.

One of the farmers asked, "Where is wolf ?"

"I was just joking, there is no wolf here."
The boy started laughing.

Farmers scolded the shepherd and went back to their fields.

After some days the shepherd played the same trick again. Farmers came this time also and went back cursing him.

One day the wolf really came. Shepherd started shouting for help.

H...E...L...P...W...O...L...F!

Farmers heard the shouts of the shepherd. But they thought that he was playing the prank again.

H...E...L...P...W...O...L...F! H...E...L...P... W...O...L...F!

11

Wolf killed many of his goats.

Repenting shepherd was left with tears in his eyes.

Moral : People do not trust even the truth of a liar.

Tit for Tat

Poor Sukkhu was returning home after day's hard labour. On the way he saw a sweet shop.

(14)

From the shop the smell of sweets was coming. Sukkhu stood near the shop enjoying the smell.

Sukkhu had little money, so he satisfied himself with the smell and began to move away.

"Stop!" the sweet seller shouted, "Where are you going without paying the money?"

"Money! But I have not taken any sweet," surprised Sukkhu protested.

"But you had been enjoying the smell of my sweets! It does not come free," said the sweet seller.

An idea struck Sukkhu. He started jingling the coins in his pocket.

20

"Why are you jingling coins in your pocket? Take them out and pay." the sweet seller said.

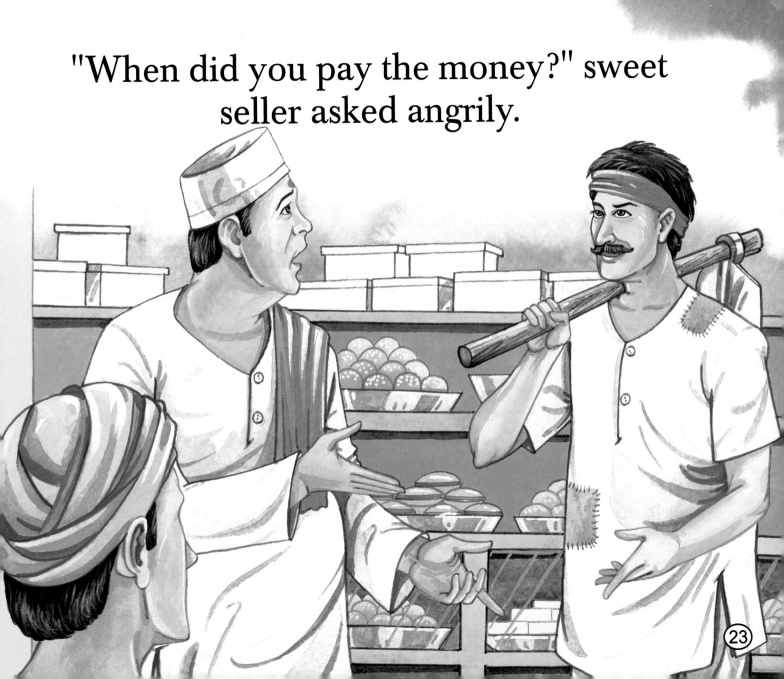

"When did you pay the money?" sweet seller asked angrily.

23

"I took in the smell of your sweets and you heard the jingle of my coins. The account is settled."

Moral : Never try to be oversmart.